A LITTLE BOOK OF CHEER

By Mary Loberg

Illustrated by Linda Welty

Hallmark Editions

A Little Book of Cheer

Sometimes when you
don't feel so good
or things don't go
just as they should...

It helps to think of cheery things--
  like a garden
        alive with butterfly wings...

Or a rainbow's promise after the rain...

And morning's gold
through your window pane.

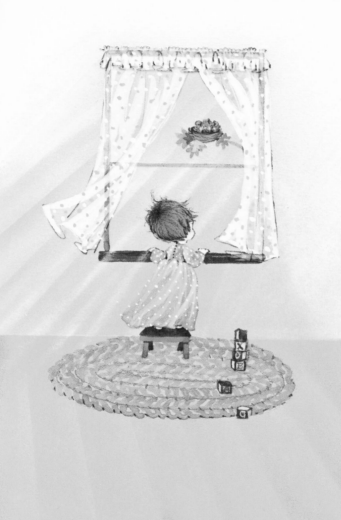

Think of fluffy kittens
who love your squeezes...

And friends who say
"bless you" after your sneezes.

It helps to remember
brooks that trickle...

And feathers that tickle!

There's a new star
to wish on
every night...

And fields of daisies
     to make your heart light.

Cheer up!
Things are never
as bad as they seem
if you dream your
favorite kind of dream.

You'll smile remembering
little girls giggling...

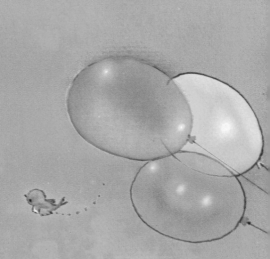

Your spirits will rise
when you think of balloons...

And little boys playing
toe-tapping tunes.

Remember the people
who can't do without you...

And letters that say,
"I've been thinking about you!"

Tomorrow you may hear
a new secret told...
or find a new friend
and a warm hand to hold.

So if you're not feeling good...
if it's raining outside
or in your heart...
Don't be blue.
Think of all the happy things
there are in the world for you.

For when you cheer up,
It cheers those who love you;
simply because
They think the world of you!